Contents

Knowing the alphabet

👁 Look in your dictionary. You will find an alphabet strip down the side of every page. You need to know the alphabet to use a dictionary.

Use this activity to find out how well you know the alphabet.

1 Fill in the missing letters of the alphabet.

a b c ____ e ____ g h ____ j ____ l

m ____ o p ____ r s t ____ v ____ x ____ z

2 Write the letter that comes **after** each pair of letters below.

e f ____   m n ____   q r ____   b c ____

u v ____   h i ____   k l ____   w x ____

3 Write the letter that comes **before** each pair of letters below.

____ t u   ____ y z   ____ g h   ____ b c

____ m n   ____ v w   ____ e f   ____ k l

4 Write the letter that comes **between** each pair of letters below.

d ____ f   o ____ q   g ____ i   r ____ t

m ____ o   u ____ w   j ____ l   x ____ z

✅ **I know the order of the letters in the alphabet.**

Understanding alphabetical order

A dictionary lists lots of words. The words listed are called **headwords**.

👁 Look in your dictionary. The headwords are listed in alphabetical order. Headwords starting with **a** come first, then headwords starting with **b**, then **c** – and so on.

Below are six lists of words. Are the words in each list in alphabetical order? Put a tick or a cross in the box.

1
ant   **b**ee   **c**at   **d**og

2
fingers   **h**ead   **l**eg   **n**eck

3   **S**unday   **M**onday   **T**uesday   **W**ednesday

4   **r**ed   **y**ellow   **p**ink   **g**reen

5   **f**og   **r**ain   **s**un   **w**ind

6   **s**even   **e**ight   **n**ine   **t**en

7   **d**ish   **j**ug   **p**late   **s**poon

8   **r**at   **b**at   **h**at   **f**at

9   **t**wo   **f**our   **s**ix   **e**ight

10   **b**ark   **g**runt   **m**oo   **q**uack

✅ **I know what alphabetical order means.**

Putting words in alphabetical order 1

First letter order

You are going to put each row of words below into alphabetical order.
👁 Remember to look at the **first letter** of each word. Think what order those letters come in the alphabet. Write the words on the line.

1

fish   **p**anda   **o**wl   **r**abbit

_____

2

teddy   **y**o-yo   **j**igsaw   **b**all

_____

3   blue   yellow   red   green

_____

4   lorry   car   bus   van

_____

5   run   jump   sing   hop

_____

✔ **I can put words into alphabetical order using their first letters.**

Finding your way around 1

The headwords that start a new section

👁 Look in your dictionary. Look at the words listed. Remember, they are called **headwords**. The headwords are in dark blue.

First come all the headwords starting with **a**, then the headwords starting with **b**, then **c**, and so on. Look for the **big red letters**. These show you where a new letter starts.

Find the **first** headword in your dictionary starting with each of the letters shown below. Remember to look for the **big red letters**. Then find the headword that starts the new section.

1 The first word starting with **b** is _____

2 The first word starting with **e** is _____

3 The first word starting with **k** is _____

4 The first word starting with **i** is _____

5 The first word starting with **m** is _____

6 The first word starting with **o** is _____

7 The first word starting with **l** is _____

8 The first word starting with **q** is _____

9 The first word starting with **r** is _____

10 The first word starting with **u** is _____

11 The first word starting with **x** is _____

12 The first word starting with **z** is _____

✓ **I can find words starting with the letter of the alphabet that I am given.**

Finding your way around 2

The alphabet strip

👁 Open your dictionary to any page. The alphabet strip shows you what letter you are in. It can help you decide if you need to go forward or back to find the letter you want.

Now play this new dictionary game. Try opening your dictionary to a page showing headwords that start with the letters below.

- You win **5 points** if you do it on the **first** go.
- You win **3 points** if you do it on the **second** go.
- You win **1 point** if you do it on the **third** go.

	Open your dictionary to headwords starting with:	How many goes you needed	Points
1	b		
2	t		
3	m		
4	e		
5	w		
6	c		
7	l		
8	s		
	Add up the points to find out your total score:		

✓ **I can open my dictionary to headwords that start with a given letter.**

Finding a word 1

Say, think and look

This is how to find a word in a dictionary.

- **Say** the word.
- **Think** what letter it starts with.
- 👁 **Look** in your dictionary for the words starting with that letter.

Then look through the headwords in blue to find the word you want.

Find in your dictionary the word that goes with each of these pictures. Write the word on the line below.

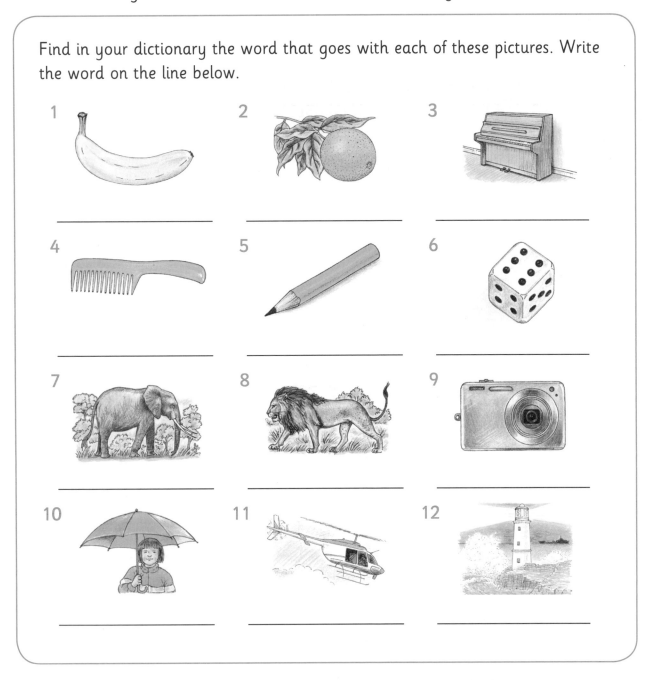

1

2

3

4

5

6

7

8

9

10

11

12

✔ **I can find a word in the dictionary by using its first letter.**

Looking through headwords

A dictionary lists lots of words. Each section has **headwords** that start with the same letter. You can quickly look down the lists of headwords to find the words you want.

👁 Look in your dictionary. The headwords are in dark blue so they stand out. You can quickly look down the list.

Follow the instructions below.
See how quickly you can find the things asked for.

1 Look quickly through all the **d** words to find **three animals**.

2 Look quickly through all the **f** words to find **three parts of the body**.

3 Look quickly through all the **b** words to find **three things with wheels**.

4 Look quickly through all the **p** words to find **six things to eat**.

5 Look quickly through all the **s** words to find **six things to wear**.

✅ **I can quickly look down a list to find the words I am looking for.**

Checking spelling 1

Just look it up!

You can use a dictionary to help you check your spelling.

👁 The dictionary shows you the right way to spell a word.

Find the correct spelling for the words shown in **bold**. Write the correct spelling at the end of the sentence.

1 Mr Brown likes to dig in his **gardin**. _____

2 The big bad wolf hid in the **forist**. _____

3 On Friday I went to a **partee**. _____

4 There was a little **boiy** called Jack. _____

5 The king looked at the **clok**. _____

6 Do you like to **danse**? _____

7 A big **rockit** flew across the sky. _____

8 Mum showed me a new **stich**. _____

✓ **I can use a dictionary to help me check my spelling.**

Spelling focus 1

Long vowel sounds

Some long vowel sounds can be spelt in different ways. You can use your dictionary to check that you have the right spelling for a word.

👁 Now look at your dictionary. You can use it help you spell correctly the words given below. Find the word that matches the picture. Then fill in the missing letters.

1 b __ __ r

2 s __ __ p

3 l __ __ f

4 ch __ __ r

5 b __ __ t

6 g __ __ t

7 sn __ __ l

8 p __ __

9 sh __ __ ld

10 gr __ __ p

11 c __ rls

12 p __ rse

✅ **I can use a dictionary to find the right spelling of a word.**

Finding the meaning

A dictionary tells you the **meaning** of each word listed.

👁 Look in your dictionary. Look at one of the headwords shown in blue. Below the headword you will see its meaning.

👁 Use your dictionary to answer the questions below. It will tell you what each word means. Write the meaning of the word next to the question.

1   What is an **acrobat**? _____

2   What is a **menu**? _____

3   What is a **taxi**? _____

_____

4   What is a **lifeboat**? _____

_____

5   What is a **chef**? _____

6   What are **noodles**? _____

_____

7   What is a **swan**? _____

8   What is a **wafer**? _____

✅ **I can use a dictionary to find out what a word means.**

Answering questions

A dictionary can help you to **find out** about things.

👁 Use your dictionary to find the answers to these questions.

Look up the word in **bold** print. Read carefully the meaning of the word.
Use it to answer the question. Write your answer on the line.

Animals

1 Can a **beetle** fly? _____

2 What does a **tadpole** become? _____

3 What does a **caterpillar** become? _____

Plants

4 Why do we grow **herbs**? _____

5 When does a **primrose** have flowers? _____

Cooking

6 What is a **cake** made from? _____

_____

7 How do you make **soup**? _____

_____

Being outdoors

8 Why do we need **bridges**? _____

_____

9 What does a **river** flow into? _____

10 Why do we have **farms**? _____

_____

✔ **I can use a dictionary to find the answer to a question.** ☐

Checking information

👁 Look in your dictionary to check whether the information in each statement below is correct. Write **TRUE** if the information is right. Write **FALSE** if it is wrong.

1 Bread is made from flour.

2 The moon goes around the earth.

3 You grow tulips from seeds.

4 A badger lives in a tree.

5 A skyscraper is a little plane.

6 A hare is like a small rabbit with little ears.

7 A tusk is a long, slightly curved and pointed tooth.

8 A potato grows on top of the ground.

9 All blackbirds have black feathers.

10 A toadstool is a rock or stone.

11 A ladybird is a small beetle.

12 An octopus has ten legs.

Well done! You have now taken your first steps in learning to use a dictionary.

✓ **I can use a dictionary to check information.**

Putting words in alphabetical order 2

Second letter order

A dictionary has lots of headwords starting with the same letter. When words have the same first letter you use the second letter to put them in alphabetical order.

Look at these lists of words. The first two letters of each word are in **bold**. Put each row of words in alphabetical order. Write them on the line.

👁 Then look up the words in your dictionary to see if you are right.

1

bird   **bu**cket   **ba**th

_____

2   **pi**llow   **pl**ease   **pe**nny   **pu**ddle   **py**ramid   **po**cket

_____

3   **es**cape   **eg**g   **ex**cellent   **ed**ge   **en**ter   **ev**en

_____

4   **sl**ope   **sk**ate   **sn**ore   **sh**elter   **sc**hool   **sm**udge

_____

5   **fi**nish   **fl**oat   **fr**eeze   **fa**rmer   **fo**otball   **fe**ast

_____

✅ **I can put words beginning with the same letter into alphabetical order.**

Finding a word 2

First and second letters

To find a word quickly, think about the **first** and **second** letters of the word.

👁 Open your dictionary to the words starting with the **first** letter. Then flick through the pages looking for words starting with the **first** and **second** letter.

Say the words to go with these pictures. Write in the **first** and **second** letters. Then find the words in your dictionary and write in the rest of the word.

1

2

3

4

5

6

7

8

9

10

11

12

✅ **I can use the first and second letters of a word to help me find it in my dictionary.**

Using guide words

👁 Open your dictionary to any page. Look in the top corners. In each corner you will see a dark blue box with white letters in it. The white words are **guide words**. One guide word is the **first** word on that page. The other guide word is the **last** word on that page.

Look at the guide words as you flick through your dictionary. These words can help you find the page you need.

1 Flick through your dictionary from the **front**. Look at the **guide words** in the top corners. Stop when you see a word starting with the letters shown below. Write the word in the box.

a be_____ [   ]   f pr_____ [   ]

b ch_____ [   ]   g se_____ [   ]

c dr_____ [   ]   h sl_____ [   ]

d fi_____ [   ]   i tr_____ [   ]

e mo_____ [   ]   j wa_____ [   ]

2 Flick through your dictionary from the **back**. Look at the **guide words** in the top corners. Stop when you see a word starting with the letters shown below. Write the word in the box.

a to_____ [   ]   f he_____ [   ]

b st_____ [   ]   g gr_____ [   ]

c sc_____ [   ]   h di_____ [   ]

d pe_____ [   ]   i cl_____ [   ]

e lo_____ [   ]   j ba_____ [   ]

✅ **I can flick through my dictionary and use the guide words at the top of the pages to find my way around.** [ ]

Scanning for words

When you **scan** you let your eyes move quickly down the page. You just look for the word you need. You don't read every word. Scanning helps you find words quickly.

Read each clue below and look at the letters given. Try and work out what the word might be.

👁 Then look in your dictionary. Find the word using scanning. Check the spelling and meaning. Then write in the missing letters. Then do the same with the next one.

1 **au** _ _ _ _ _   **Clue**: the season between summer and winter

2 **li** _ _ _ _ _ _   **Clue**: a room or building where books are kept

3 **fo** _ _ _ _   **Clue**: to go or come after

4 **br** _ _ _ _ _ _ _   **Clue**: the first meal of the day

5 **fu** _ _ _ _ _ _ _   **Clue**: chairs, tables, beds and other such objects used around your home

6 **st** _ _ _ _ _   **Clue**: where your food goes after you swallow it

7 **en** _ _ _ _ _ _ _   **Clue**: very large

8 **te** _ _ _ _ _ _   **Clue**: very bad

9 **ho** _ _ _ _ _ _   **Clue**: a place where sick people are cared for

10 **ne** _ _ _ _ _ _ _   **Clue**: a person who lives next door or quite near

11 **ga** _ _ _ _   **Clue**: a place where cars are kept

12 **wh** _ _ _ _ _ _ _ _ _   **Clue**: a small cart that you use to carry things (in the garden, for example)

✔ **I can scan a page to find a headword quickly.**

Exploring definitions

A dictionary gives the **meaning** of each word listed. This is called the **definition**. A good definition helps you to understand the word better.

Here are some words and simple, quick definitions.

👁 Look in your dictionary. Find the full definition for each word and write it in the box.

	Word	Quick definition	Full dictionary definition
1	scissors	used for cutting	
2	vegetable	a bit of a plant	
3	elbow	a bit of your arm	
4	church	a building	
5	draughts	a game you play	
6	aquarium	a tank	
7	expert	a clever person	
8	bungalow	a type of house	

Now answer this question.

9	Question	Why are the dictionary definitions better?
	Answer	

✔ **I can use dictionary definitions to help me understand the meaning of a word.**

More than one meaning

Some words have more than one meaning so the dictionary gives you more than one definition.

👁 Look in your dictionary and find a word with more than one meaning. You will see that there is a coloured number beside each definition.

Use your dictionary to find the two meanings of each of these words.

1	**ball**	meaning:
		meaning:
2	**coach**	meaning:
		meaning:
3	**pepper**	meaning:
		meaning:
4	**spell**	meaning:
		meaning:
5	**bark**	meaning:
		meaning:

✓ **I know that a headword in a dictionary may sometimes have more than one definition – because the word has more than one meaning.**

Making a glossary

Some information books have a **glossary**. A glossary gives **definitions** of topic words used in the book. These are special words that you might not know. The words in a glossary are listed in alphabetical order.

Here are the words to go in a glossary for a book about animals.

| hatch | vet | ~~burrow~~ | tame | den | flock |
| cub | pet | whiskers | chick | limb | foal |

Write the glossary. First write the words in alphabetical order in the 'Word' column below.

👁 Then look up each word in your dictionary. Use the dictionary to help you write each definition. The first word and definition have been written in for you.

	Word	Definition
1	burrow	a tunnel dug underground by an animal such as a rabbit
2		
3		
4		
5		
6		
7		
8		
9		
10		
11		
12		

✓ **I can use a dictionary to help me make a glossary of special interest words.**

Finding the meaning

Sometimes you hear or read words that you have not met before. You may not know what they mean but you can look them up in your dictionary. The **definitions** will help you understand the words.

You might find these words in a book about places.

👁 Look in your dictionary to find out what each word means. Write the meaning in the box.

	Word	Meaning
1	bay	
2	valley	
3	harbour	
4	reservoir	
5	dam	
6	canal	
7	fort	
8	cliff	
9	quarry	
10	igloo	
11	export	
12	famine	

✓ **I can use a dictionary to help me understand new words.**

Checking the meaning

Sometimes you can work out what a word means from **how it is used** in a sentence. You can then look in a dictionary to check if you are right.

Read these sentences. Try to work out the **meaning** of the word in **bold** print.
Write the meaning in the box.

👁 Then look in your dictionary to see if you are right. Correct your definition if you need to.

1   The blackbird is a **common** garden bird.

   | **common** means: |
   | |

2   The next day the sun came out and the ice began to **thaw**.

   | **thaw** means: |
   | |

3   She found that the tree was **hollow**. A perfect hiding place!

   | **hollow** means: |
   | |

4   Suddenly the door opened. Joe had to **duck** behind the bushes.

   | **duck** means: |
   | |

5   It had been a long hard winter and food was **scarce**.

   | **scarce** means: |
   | |

✅ **I can work out the meaning of words using the text and a dictionary.**

Finding facts 1

Quick and easy

You can use a dictionary to find some quick facts about a topic.

👁 Use your dictionary to find out about these subjects. Write **two** facts about each one.

1

Mushrooms

Fact a:
Fact b:

2

Rice

Fact a:
Fact b:

3 **The lungs**

Fact a:
Fact b:

4 **The penguin**

Fact a:
Fact b:

5 **The violin**

Fact a:
Fact b:

6 **The crocodile**

Fact a:
Fact b:

✓ **I can use a dictionary to quickly find out facts about a given subject.**

Looking for key words

A dictionary can help you to answer questions. First you must decide on the key word or words in the question. Then you can look these words up in your dictionary.

Here is a quiz. Underline the key word or words in each quiz question.

Then look the words up in your dictionary. Use facts from the dictionary definition to help you write your answer.

1

Question: What is chocolate made from?

Answer:

2

Question: Why does a ship need an anchor?

Answer:

3 **Question**: When does the festival of Eid take place?

Answer:

4 **Question**: Where does cotton come from?

Answer:

5 **Question**: What does a hawk eat?

Answer:

6 **Question**: What do the muscles in our body do?

Answer:

7 **Question**: What ingredients do you need to make a pancake?

Answer:

8 **Question**: Is a spider an insect? Give a reason for your answer.

Answer:

✔ **I can identify the key words in a question and look them up in a dictionary.**

Reading carefully

You need to think hard about a definition to check that you really understand it.

Read these questions. Look up the key word or words in your dictionary. Think very carefully about the definitions. Then write your answer in the box below the question.

1

Question: Why do fish need fins?

Answer:

2

Question: Why is a bus a type of transport?

Answer:

3 **Question**: Why isn't there a rainbow every time it rains?

Answer:

4 **Question**: Why is the cuckoo called the cuckoo?

Answer:

5 **Question**: Why isn't chalk a good building material?

Answer:

6 **Question**: Why is the heart an important part of the body?

Answer:

7 **Question**: Why do we recycle rubbish?

Answer:

8 **Question**: Why is the London underground railway sometimes called 'the tube'?

Answer:

✅ **I can think carefully about the definitions given in a dictionary.**

Finding facts 2

More information

A dictionary tells you what a word means but it does not give you lots of information.

Use your dictionary to help you fill in this information chart. Your dictionary will give you some information, but it will not give you all the information. There will be some gaps.

	Animal	What it looks like	Where it lives	What it eats
1	hippopotamus			
2	zebra			
3	kangaroo			
4	eagle			
5	giraffe			
6	turtle			

Now write your answer to the question below.

7 Where could you look for the information that is still missing from the chart above? _____

I know what information I can find in a dictionary and I know where to look for more information.

Spelling focus 2

The 'w' special

A dictionary can help you to spell **difficult words**.

Use the clues to help you work out the words below.

👁 Look in your dictionary to check the spelling. Then put the missing letter or letters in each word.

1 **Picture clue**:

w＿llet

2 **Picture clue**:

w＿nd

3 **Picture clue**:

w＿sh

4 | What is special about the spelling of these words?

5 **Picture clue**:

w＿rm

6 **Picture clue**:

w＿rld

7 **Clue**: letters put together so that they mean something

w＿rd

8 **Clue**: something you do; your job

w＿＿k

9 **Clue**: not as good as; less well

w＿＿se

10 **Clue**: value

w＿＿th

11 | What is special about the spelling of these words?

✓ **I can use a dictionary to help me spell difficult words.**

Spelling focus 3

Tricky graphemes

A **grapheme** is one or more **letters** that make a **sound**.

1 👁 Use your dictionary to find words that begin with these tricky
graphemes. Write the words in the box.

a **kn**

b **wr**

c **wh**

d **ph**

e **ex**

2 👁 Now use your dictionary to find the letter that is missing from the end
of each of these words.

a **thum** ___   d **com** ___

b **crum** ___   e **clim** ___

c **bom** ___   f **lam** ___

✅ **I can use a dictionary to find words with tricky graphemes.**

Checking spelling 2

Spelling choice

There are different ways of spelling many sounds. A dictionary will help you make the right spelling choice.

Which spellings of these words are correct?

👁 Check each spelling in your dictionary. Then draw a circle round the spelling that is correct.

1 **shef** or **chef**

2 **fense** or **fence**

3 **gerbil** or **jerbil**

4 **sity** or **city**

5 **scooter** or **skooter**

6 **bridje** or **bridge**

7 **engine** or **enjine**

8 **magic** or **majic**

9 **nurce** or **nurse**

10 **price** or **prise**

11 **parcel** or **parsel**

12 **geans** or **jeans**

✔ **I can use a dictionary to help me make the right choice of spelling.**

Checking spelling 3

Your own writing

You can use your dictionary to check your own spelling.

Read each of these sentences. Underline the word that looks wrong.

👁 Use your dictionary to check the spelling. Write the correct spelling in the box.

1

Grace is Ruby's best frend.

2

The clowns
made everyone laff.

3 We must give the plants warter.

4 Today we dressed up in diffrent clothes.

5 There were lots of peeple running away.

6 I hope my story will plees Mrs Jenkins.

7 This is the story of a littul puppy.

8 I knew the anser at once.

9 When you have finished, look carefully at the correct spellings. Underline the tricky bit in each word. Try to remember it. Then ask someone to test you.

✓ **I can use a dictionary to check the spellings in my writing.**

Checking spelling 4

Proof reading

Joe wants to tell his granddad about his day out. He has written a letter. Before he sends the letter he needs to check his spelling. Help Joe to check his letter. Underline any words that look wrong. Use your dictionary to find the correct spelling. Write it above the spelling that is wrong. Doing these things is called **proof reading**.

Clue: there are 15 wrong spellings.

Dear Granddad,

We had a great time at the theem park. I loved all the rides but Jack

did not like the noyse. The musick was too lowd for him. The best

ride was Spaseship 101. We went in a rockit and I was very exsited.

After that we had huge ise creams. You could have any flavor. I

had strawburry and Jack had chockerlate. Then we saw a show

with acrobats and a juggeler and a groop of clowns. The clowns ran

around with buckits full of water.

Will you come and vissit us soon? I hope so.

Lots of love, from

Joe

 I can use a dictionary to help me check the spelling of words.

Summing up

How a dictionary is organised

Your dictionary is set out so that you can find words quickly.

Use this page to remind yourself how a dictionary is arranged.

👁 Look at the feature that each arrow is pointing to. Write a label to explain how this feature helps you to find words in your dictionary. Then move on to the next feature.

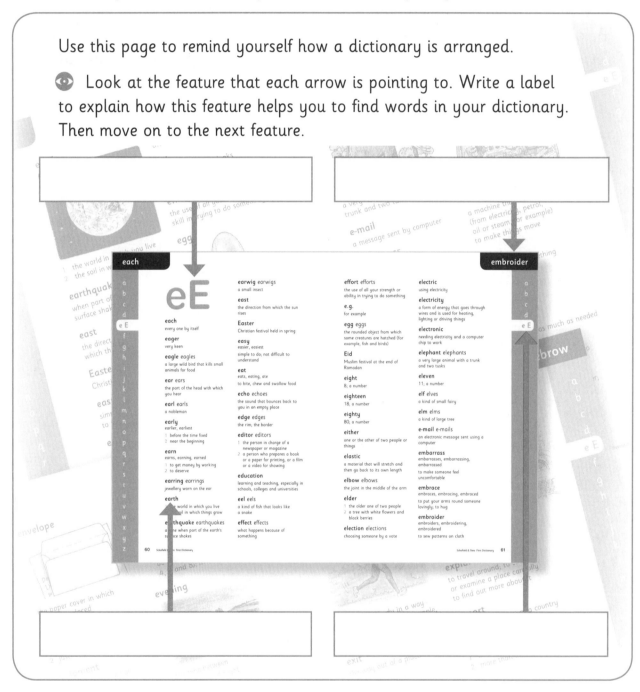

Well done! You have now learnt more about how to use a dictionary. Next you will learn how to use a thesaurus.

✓ **I can explain how the layout and organisation of a dictionary help me to find words quickly.**

What is a thesaurus?

A thesaurus is a **collection of words**. A thesaurus gives you a list of words that mean **the same** or **nearly the same** as the word you look up.

👁 Look through your thesaurus. Look at how it is organised. Look at how the words are set out. Then read the statements below. Tick each statement that is true. Put a cross by each statement that is false.

1 The headwords are listed in alphabetical order. ☐

2 Headwords starting with **ab__** come before headwords starting with **ac__**. ☐

3 There is an alphabet strip on every page. ☐

4 The headwords listed are in bold black print to make them stand out. ☐

5 Underneath each headword is a definition. ☐

6 Underneath each headword is a list of words that mean the same. ☐

7 The first headword on a page is shown in the top corner. ☐

8 The last headword on a page is shown in the top corner. ☐

9 The headwords are listed in columns. ☐

10 A thesaurus is a fiction book. ☐

11 A thesaurus has an index. ☐

12 A thesaurus is full of facts. ☐

✔ **I know what a thesaurus is and how it is set out.** ☐

Finding words in a thesaurus

A thesaurus gives you words that mean **the same** or **nearly the same** as the word that you are looking up. 👁 Look at a black headword in your thesaurus. You will see a list of words underneath. They mean the same or nearly the same.

👁 Find these headwords in the thesaurus. Write down the words that are listed.

Headword	Words that mean nearly the same
1 hot	
2 sob	
3 hurry	
4 cosy	
5 far	
6 new	
7 tug	
8 jolt	

✓ **I can look up a word in my thesaurus to find other words that mean the same or nearly the same.**

Finding synonyms – feelings

Words with the same or nearly the same meaning are called **synonyms**.
A thesaurus gives you a list of synonyms for each headword.

Draw faces to show the feelings described below.

Then use your thesaurus to find synonyms for each feelings word.

I feel **happy**.

Synonyms for **happy**:

_____
_____
_____
_____

I feel **sad**.

Synonyms for **sad**:

_____
_____
_____
_____

I feel **afraid**.

Synonyms for **afraid**:

_____
_____
_____
_____

I feel **angry**.

Synonyms for **angry**:

_____
_____
_____
_____

✔ **I can use a thesaurus to find synonyms for words.**

Similar but not the same

The words given in a thesaurus do not all have exactly the same meaning.

👁 Look up these action words in your thesaurus. Copy down the synonyms that the thesaurus gives you. Imagine that you are doing the action that goes with each synonym. Think about the differences between the meanings of each synonym.

1 **pull**

2 **talk**

3 **cut**

4 **jump**

5 **throw**

6 **hit**

✔ **I know that the words I find in a thesaurus do not have exactly the same meaning.**

Using a different word

A thesaurus can help you when you are writing. It gives you new words to use.

Read these sentences.

👁 Look up in your thesaurus the word that is in **bold** print. Choose one of the synonyms to use instead. Write it in the box.

1 On the table was some **tasty** food.

2 The wizard was an **unkind** man.

3 It was a **silly** thing to do.

4 Mr Brown was very **rich**.

5 Fatima began to **eat** her picnic.

6 The machine began to **shake**.

7 The noise seemed to **scare** the people.

8 The room was **dark**.

9 There was a **terrible** crash.

10 Suddenly there was a **flash** of light.

✅ **I can use a thesaurus to find a different word to use in a sentence.**

Choosing the right meaning

Some words have more than one meaning. When this happens, the thesaurus gives you more than one list of synonyms. Each list has a number in front of it. Here is an example.

- 👁 Look in your thesaurus for the word **cold**.
- Look at the bright green numbers.
- The numbers show that there are **two lists of words**. This is because the word has **two meanings**.

Read these sentences. 👁 Look up the word in **bold** print and choose a synonym to use instead of it. Think about the meaning. Make sure you choose a word from the correct list. When you are sure, write your synonym in the box.

1 It was a **gloomy** day.

2 He was feeling **gloomy**.

3 It was a **hard** puzzle.

4 The piece of wood felt **hard**.

5 There was a **bright** light in the room.

6 She seems to be quite **bright**.

7 He was a tall **thin** man.

8 The soup was **thin** and tasteless.

✅ **I can think about the meaning of a word and choose synonyms from the correct list.**

Choosing interesting words

Sometimes we use dull everyday words in our writing. A thesaurus can help us to use **more interesting words**.

The words shown in **bold** print in the sentences below are not very interesting. 👁 Look in your thesaurus for one more interesting word to replace each of them. Remember to think about the meaning and choose carefully. Write the word on the line.

1   The people were scared and

   began to **shout** _____.

2   Once there was a very **bad** _____ little girl called Beryl.

3   Old Jack was a **good** _____ man.

4   Winifred the witch was rather **fat** _____.

5   The metal was **hot** _____.

6   The troll was a **nasty** _____ creature.

Remember: some words have more than one meaning. When you look up these words, make sure that you choose from the correct list of synonyms.

7   Some of the children

   began to **cry** _____.

8   Mum was **mad** _____ when she saw the mess.

 I can use a thesaurus to find interesting words for my own writing.

Varying your words

Sometimes when you write you find that you have used the same word over and over again. It makes the writing sound boring. You can use a thesaurus to find **different words** to use.

Read each of these story openings. Circle the word that is used several times. 👁 Look in your thesaurus for different words to use. Write your choices above the words you have circled.

1 Once there was a little cottage with a little door and two little windows. Outside the front door was a little plant pot.

2 Giant Jim had big feet, big teeth, a big tummy and a big smile. He lived in a big castle with many big rooms.

3 Mrs Gill was a very nice old lady. She lived in a nice house in a nice part of town.

4 The monster had a horrible face. It was covered in horrible warts. He also had two horrible tusks and hundreds of horrible teeth. He let out a horrible cry.

✅ **I can use a thesaurus to vary the words I use in my writing.**

Collecting words 1

Writing a poem

A thesaurus is very helpful when you are **writing a poem or a description**.
It can help you choose interesting words.

Use your thesaurus to add some interesting words to this word collection.

👁 Look up in your thesaurus the words in the boxes below. Choose words
that will help you describe what a **butterfly** looks like and how it moves.

quick	**quiet**	**delicate**
fly		**float**
bright	**nice patterns**	lots of **colours**

✅ **I can use a thesaurus to help me choose good describing words to use in a description or poem.**

Collecting words 2

Word tree

A thesaurus is full of exciting new words.

Look in your thesaurus for some different words to add to this word tree. Find **three** exciting new words for each word given. Write the new words on the leaf.

shy

keen

brave

strong

calm

careful

ugly

dirty

strange

unkind

I can use a thesaurus to find and choose exciting words.

Making a word store

It is a good idea to **collect** interesting words. Then you can use them whenever you need them. Why not start a **writing journal**? Try using each page for different types of words.

  Use your thesaurus to find synonyms for the words below. Collect the most interesting words that you can find. Make sure that you write the words on the correct page of the notebook shown below. One page is for words that describe movement. The other page is for words that describe speech.

creep	jump	growl	laugh	rush
walk	scream	moan	tell	stagger

Words to describe how
things move

Words to describe how
people speak

✅ **I can use a thesaurus to help me build up a collection of exciting words.**

Making the best choice

A thesaurus can help a writer to choose the best words. More than one word will often fit. The writer must decide which word is just right.

Read the sentences below. In each sentence, the writer is not sure about the word in **bold** print.

👁 Use your thesaurus to find **three** other words that could be used. Write the words in the box. Circle the word that **you** would choose.

1

Trees **shake** in the angry wind.

2

The factory will **spoil** the area.

3 Waves **sparkle** in the sunlight.

4 Ben tried to **grab** the bottle.

5 He spoke in a **loud** voice.

6 **Put** the shapes on the tray.

Well done! You now know how to use a thesaurus.

✓ **I can think about different words and choose the word that fits best.**